Contents

In this comic ...

Little sis

Billy

We Can Fly!

One Saturday, Billy and his little sister learnt how to get super powers!

I am a wizard. Say my name, Shazam, and you will transform!

Thanks, sir!

Shazam!

Shazam!

Now I am Captain Marvel! I can fly!

I can fly like Supergirl!

Captain Marvel and his little sister can search for problems and fight for good!

But sometimes they do not feel like it.

Just Let Me Sleep!

Early one Thursday morning ...

Wake up! We have a job!

What on earth is that?

Yuck! So dirty!

Ick!

Out! I am asleep!

You need a cleaner!

Get up!

Just a bit longer, little sis.

It is seven-thirty!

You heard me! Get up!

NO!

But the town needs us!

Okay! I am up.

The flames were as high as the sky!

They heard a cry from inside.

whoosh!

There! I am glad that is over!

Thanks, sir! Now we must find out who started the blaze.

I will find out.

Captain Marvel Is Off!